A Treasure Island

Story by Dawn McMillan   Illustrations by Susy Boyer Rigby

Gran and Meg ran down the beach.

"Gran! Look at this big rock!"

shouted Meg.

"It looks like an island!"

4

Gran said,

"It looks like a treasure island!

Who will find the treasure first?"

"I will!" shouted Meg.

Meg climbed onto the rock.

She looked and looked
for the treasure.

"I can't find it, Gran," she said.
"Please come and help me."

"Here I come!" said Gran.

Gran and Meg climbed up the rock.

They sat down at the top.

Gran said,

"I can see the treasure!"

"Where? Where?" shouted Meg.

"It's over here," said Gran.

"Look down in this rock pool."

Meg looked into the little pool.

"I can see a starfish," she said.

"It's by the red seaweed!"

12

"Gran!" shouted Meg.

"Look! A crab!

I can see a big green crab.

Can I take it home?"

Gran said,

"The starfish and the crab

are treasures, Meg,

and the seaweed is, too.

But they all have to stay here

in the pool."

"This **is** a treasure island,"

said Meg,

"and we did find the treasure!"